MOUNTAINS

SCOTLAND'S LIVING LANDSCAPES

SCOTTISH NATURAL HERITAGE

© Scottish Natural Heritage 2002

ISBN 1 85397 326 2 paperback

A CIPO record is held at the British Library

HS4K1002

Acknowledgements: John Mackay, Des Thompson, John Gordon, John Baxter

Author: Mark Wrightham (SNH)

Series Editor: John Baxter (SNH)

Design and production: Iain Sarjeant, SNH Design and Publications

Photography:

S.Austin cover bottom centre, 22, 25 top left, 25 bottom right, N.Benvie 20 top left, L.Campbell cover top left, cover bottom left, 15 top left, 16, 21 bottom right, 23 top, 24, 25 top right, 25 bottom left, L.Gill/SNH 1, 3, 6, 7 bottom, 10 top,11, 12, 13, 14 left, 15 top right, 17, 18, 19 left, 19 right, 20 bottom right, 21 top left, 21 top right, 21 bottom left, 36, B.Grant 30 bottom, J.Hyde/ B&C Alexander 8, P&A.Macdonald cover right, insert opp foreword, introduction, 2, 5, 7 top, 9, 10 bottom, 29 right, N.McIntyre 14 right, 29 left, 32, J.Macpherson inside cover page, 33, 34, 35, K.Ringland 23 bottom right, I.Sarjeant contents page, 30 top, G.Satterley 28, S.Whitehorne 26, M.Wrightham 4, 31.

Illustration:

E.Charman/SNH map, JMW.Turner c National Gallery of Scotland, Loch Coruisk, Skye 27.

Scottish Natural Heritage

Design and Publications

Battleby

Redgorton

Perth PH1 3EW

Tel: 01738 444177

Fax: 01738 827411

E-mail: pubs@snh.gov.uk

Web site: http://www.snh.org.uk

Cover photographs (clockwise from top left):
1. Golden eagle
2. Loch Einich in the western Cairngorms
3. Mountain hare
4. Creeping azalea on an exposed ridge

MOUNTAINS

SCOTLAND'S LIVING LANDSCAPES

by

Mark Wrightham

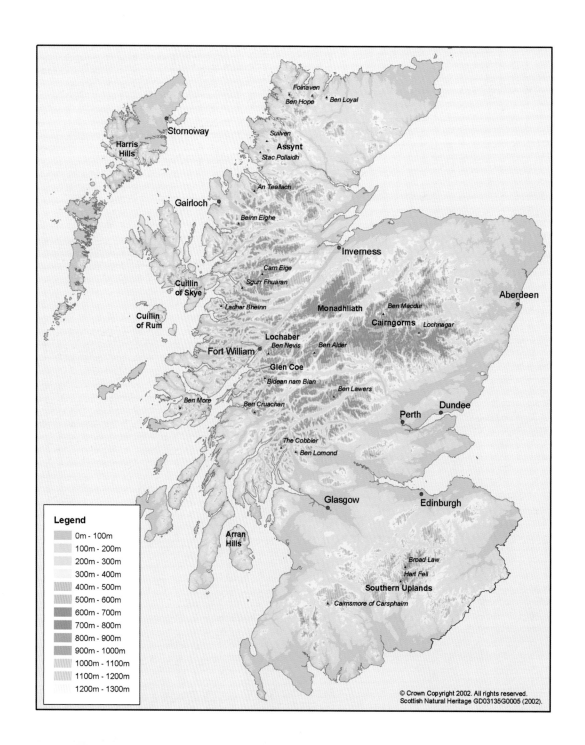

Foinaven
Ben Hope • Ben Loyal

Stornoway

Harris
Hills

Suilven
Assynt
Stac Pollaidh

An Teallach

Gairloch

Beinn Eighe

Inverness

Aberdeen

Carn Eige

Sgurr Fhuaran

Cuillin
of Skye

Ben Macdui
Ladhar Bheinn
Monadhliath
Cairngorms
Lochnagar

Cuillin
of Rum

Lochaber
Ben Nevis   Ben Alder
Fort William

Glen Coe

Bidean nam Bian
Ben Lawers

Ben More
Perth   Dundee
Ben Cruachan

The Cobbler
Ben Lomond

Glasgow
Edinburgh

Arran
Hills

Broad Law
Hart Fell

Southern Uplands
Cairnsmore of Carsphairn

Legend

	0m - 100m
	100m - 200m
	200m - 300m
	300m - 400m
	400m - 500m
	500m - 600m
	600m - 700m
	700m - 800m
	800m - 900m
	900m - 1000m
	1000m - 1100m
	1100m - 1200m
	1200m - 1300m

Contents

Introduction   1

The ancient foundations   2
A collision of continents   2
The volcanoes of Scotland   7

Ice sculptures   8
The Ice Age   8
Snow and glaciers   10

The mountains today   13
Trees and woodland   14
Heaths and bogs   15
Plant life on the high tops   16
Upland mammals   23
Upland birds   24
Invertebrate life   24

Mountains and people   26
Sheep walks and deer forests   29
Hillwalking and mountaineering   30
Human impacts   33

Looking ahead   34

References   37

Stac Pollaidh from Cùl Beag

Ben More and Stob Binnean

Foreword

Finally, in the year 2002, those steep sided, conspicuous landforms we call 'mountains' are being honoured as we celebrate the International Year of Mountains. Hopefully this year will help us all gain a greater appreciation of the need for more care of their spiritual qualities, their beauty and vulnerability.

Though not high mountain cloud-piercers like the European or Southern Alps of New Zealand or the Central Andes, the Scottish Highlands are high on the list of beloved mountains of the world. The pressures of development, however, are great, for these, like mountains worldwide, are economically marginalized areas. The pathway of sustainable development and conservation is difficult, but Scotland is now taking a leadership role in this approach.

A major component of sustainable development is giving areas of special value some kind of protected area status. This year, Scotland has just established its first National Park, centred on Loch Lomond and the Trossachs, and the Cairngorms National Park is in the final stages of establishment. These are splendid contributions to the International Year of Mountains.

But after the tumult of International Year of Mountains, after the conferences, workshops, and other mountain-based events of 2002 are over and done, the drive for more tender loving care for our mountains must not falter. Scotland has other significant mountain areas in need of improved conservation status. As indicated by the author of this publication: "Scotland's mountains are the most extensive near-natural areas in Britain, with many habitats, plants and animals which are rare or absent elsewhere in the world."

Scotland's literature, painting and photography bespeak the importance of its mountains as symbols of national identity. This publication will hopefully increase the knowledge of local residents and visitors from elsewhere about the Highlands of Scotland, and promote greater stewardship of these precious landscapes. The World Commission on Protected Areas congratulates you in your move to create two mountain National Parks. Why stop at two?

Lawrence S. Hamilton

Professor Lawrence S. Hamilton
Vice-Chair for Mountains
World Commission on Protected Areas
World Conservation Union (IUCN)

Between 1883 and 1904, the Scottish Meteorological Society maintained an observatory on Ben Nevis. W.T. Kilgour's account of life in the observatory was published in 1905, and well illustrates the nature of the mountain environment: "The sublimity of prospect, the variety of phenomena, the rolling mists, and the raging tempests have their own peculiar interest, and none the less enthralling is the study of gales and cloud effects, the torrential rains, the accumulation of snow, and the remarkable range and fluctuation of temperature; but the feature which probably most impresses the uninitiated is the stillness - the awful solitude - which at times prevails amid these fastnesses".

Ben Nevis

Beinn Eighe and Liathach

Introduction

Mountains and wild uplands cover two thirds of Scotland. This relatively small country straddles geological and climatic boundaries and contains several distinct mountain areas. On Skye, the Cuillin encircles Loch Coruisk with a dark wall of shattered gabbro. In Lochaber, narrow ridges of glistening quartzite plunge to deep glens with scattered birchwoods. In Sutherland, statuesque sentinels such as Suilven and Ben Loyal overlook mile after mile of gnarled wet heathland, which turns to a rich golden-brown in the autumn light. In the Cairngorms, vast boulder plateaux with granite tors rise from lower slopes of heather and pine. Winter transforms all of these mountains, bringing, by turns, the crystalline beauty of sunlit snow and ice, or arctic blizzards with driving spindrift.

Scotland's mountains may appear small alongside the Alps or Himalaya, but this comparison is deceptive. Our highest peaks extend more than 600m above the limit of tree growth and their natural environment and wildlife have much in common with summits in the Pyrenees or Norway. Long-lived snowbeds linger in the shadowy recesses of Ben Nevis and the Cairngorms.

Our mountains record the immense geological forces that shaped Scotland over millions of years. They are the most extensive near-natural areas in Britain, with many habitats, plants and animals that are rare or absent elsewhere in the world. They are well-known landmarks and symbols of national identity, enriching the lives of local residents and those who visit for recreation. But these unique mountain landscapes and their wildlife are also vulnerable to insensitive use and demand the highest standards of stewardship.

The ancient foundations

Today's mountain scene is a snapshot in a continuing process of change, and the origin of Scotland's mountains can be traced almost to the beginnings of measurable geological time.

A collision of continents

1500 million years ago, north-west Scotland was part of an ancient continent known as Laurentia. This continent included much of present-day North America and was separated from northern Europe, and the rest of Britain, by an ocean known as Iapetus.

But all this was to change, and a period of extraordinary upheaval 400-500 million years ago laid the foundations for much of the Highlands. The movement of vast plates that comprise the earth's crust forced these continents together, crushing, folding and uplifting the sedimentary rocks of the ocean floor. These rocks were drastically altered during this process, creating hard schists and slates, which formed a great mountain range known as the Caledonides. The collision of the continents also forced these rocks westwards in north-west Scotland, overriding the ancient crust for over 70km, and the resulting 'front' is marked by the line of an internationally renowned geological feature - the Moine Thrust.

The Moine Thrust near Elphin

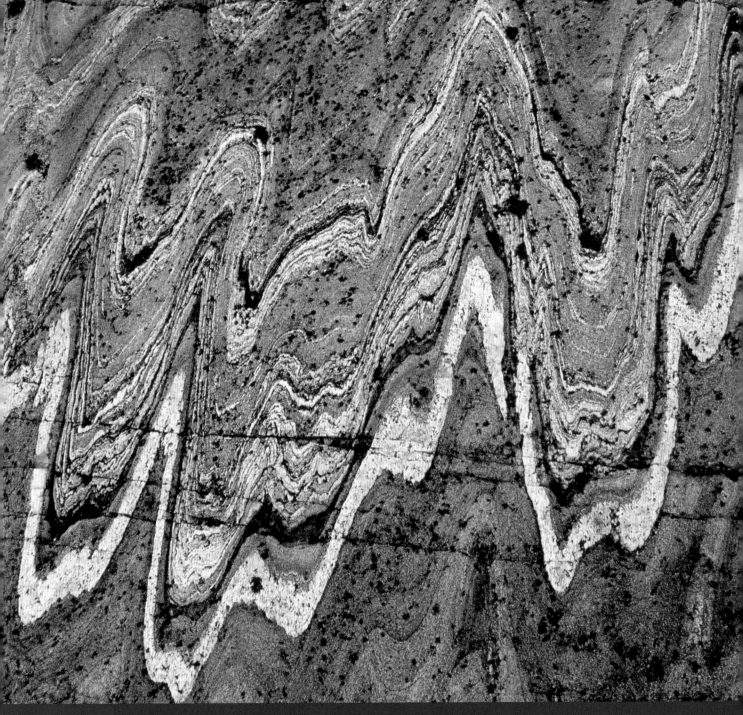

Intensely folded schist

The Moine Thrust still forms a highly visible boundary today. The mountains of Wester Ross and Sutherland lie to the north-west, consisting of Torridonian sandstone on a base of contorted Lewisian gneiss. This is one of the most ancient rocks in the world, almost three billion years old, and is the last Scottish remnant of Laurentia. These mountains are typified by the lone sculpted sandstone peaks of Suilven and Stac Pollaidh, which rise from open, rugged moorland. South-east of the Moine Thrust, the Northern and Central Highlands are dominated by more massive schist ranges such as Beinn Dearg and the Fannichs. These mountains are the worn-down roots of the Caledonides, exposed by weathering and erosion over the intervening millennia.

This collision of continents was also an important phase in the development of the Southern Uplands. As the plates carrying North America and northern Europe converged, sedimentary rocks forming part of the Iapetus ocean floor were lifted and bulldozed to form the foundations of these hills. These rocks are relatively susceptible to weathering and eroded more easily, producing rounded, rolling hills such as Broad Law and Hart Fell, near Moffat.

Beinn Dearg, south-east of the Moine Thrust

"Northwest Scotland is one of the classic areas in the annals of British geology, and its Geological Survey memoir is often claimed to be the most important ever produced".

John Whittow 1992

Suilven, north-west of the Moine Thrust

"The magnitude of the scale of nature and the utter
loneliness of the vast mountain-world powerfully affect us.
But deep beneath the feelings thus evoked lies a more or
less consciously felt mental unrest in presence of the
mystery of the cause of such stupendous features. The
stern broken features of the mountains arrest our
attention and excite our imagination as we try to picture
to ourselves how they came into existence".

Archibald Geikie 1901

Beinn Eighe, Wester Ross

The volcanoes of Scotland

The cataclysmic events 400-500 million years ago were accompanied by volcanic activity, as molten magma forced its way upwards from deep in the earth's crust. In some places this cooled slowly underground to form huge masses of granite. These rock masses, exposed by erosion, now form many of Scotland's best-known mountains, including Ben Cruachan and the Cairngorms. Elsewhere, lava flows erupted onto the earth's surface from active volcanoes and cooled rapidly to form rhyolite and andesite - now the most characteristic rocks of Glencoe and Ben Nevis. These mountains still reveal the structure of those ancient volcanoes, providing world-famous examples of a process known as 'cauldron subsidence', in which gigantic plugs of lava have partially collapsed into magma below.

The next major phase in the history of Scotland's mountains began some 60 million years ago. The land masses which now form Europe and North America were torn apart by further continental movement, triggering renewed volcanic activity. Huge fractures opened along western Scotland, spilling lava to form a great basalt plateau 4km thick. Volcanoes developed in several locations, underlain by enormous subterranean masses of gabbro and granite. Subsequent erosion has exposed these rocks, which now form the Arran Hills and the Skye and Rum Cuillin.

The raw materials were in place, but the landscape still bore little resemblance to the mountains of the present day. A further powerful influence would be crucial to the development of Scotland's trademark skylines, from the Cobbler to An Teallach.

The Cuillin, Skye

Granite

Ice sculptures

The role of ice in the shaping of mountains is relatively obvious in Nepal or Alaska, where there are still large glaciers. Similar forces also carved Scotland's mountain landscapes, but this was not appreciated until 1840, when a Swiss geologist, Louis Agassiz, published some astute detective work. Agassiz was well-acquainted with the effects of glaciation in his native land and recognised similar features, including ice-transported boulders and ice-scoured rocks, in many parts of Scotland.

The Ice Age

The last 2.5 million years have seen a succession of glaciations, in which large parts of Scotland were periodically covered by ice sheets that reached over 1000m in thickness. At other times, smaller mountain glaciers existed for long periods in the Highlands. The erosive power of these glaciers radically reshaped the underlying terrain and moulded the mountains into their present forms. Drastic changes occurred throughout the Scottish hills, but were most pronounced in the Western Highlands where snowfall was greatest and the glaciers were most active. The mountains of this area are therefore much more deeply hewn, with narrow ridges and deep glens, in contrast to the rolling plateaux of the Cairngorms and Monadhliath.

Margerie Glacier,
Glacier Bay National Park, Alaska

Glacially-dissected mountains above Strath Fillan, in the south-west Highlands

Snow and glaciers

Then as now, snow preferentially accumulated on shady north or east-facing lee slopes. Small glaciers developed in these areas, gouging out existing hollows to form much deeper corries with very steep headwalls. These glaciers merged to form great rivers of ice in lower valleys, in a scene which must have resembled the famous Mer de Glace in the French Alps. At other times, the glaciers coalesced to form vast sheets of ice, as seen in Greenland today, that buried entire mountain ranges or left only a few protruding summits. Powerful 'streams' of ice within the ice sheets also deepened the glens and, in some instances, carved new ones. In the far north-west, including Assynt, the ice sheets scoured the bedrock to create distinctive cnoc and lochan landscapes.

Periods of extensive glaciation were interspersed with phases of cold climate when glaciers were less widespread or absent. During these phases, soils were subjected to intense freezing

Glen Rosa, Arran; a valley carved by ice

and thawing. These 'periglacial' conditions are recorded on mountain slopes and summits, where some features betray the downhill creep of saturated rock debris over frozen ground below. Terraces and 'lobes' made up of soil, rock debris and coarse boulders cascade down hillsides, locked in position by the arrival of warmer weather. On some summits, piano-sized boulders have slid downhill, ploughing trenches which trail behind like meteorite tails. On the Cairngorm plateau, the heaving action of expanding ice has created delicate patterns in the fine granite gravel.

The arrival of warmer conditions loosened the grip of the last glaciers about 11,500 years ago. It is sobering to remember, however, that warm intervals like that of the present day also occurred between previous glaciations, and the Ice Age could yet return to Scotland.

Boulder lobes, Lurchers Gully, Cairngorms

Coire an Lochain in the northern Cairngorms

Foinaven as seen from Arkle, Sutherland

Scree slopes and debris cones of quartzite on Foinaven

The mountains today

The last 11,500 years have seen a relatively congenial climate, but the rocks and screes of the mountains remain in a constant state of gradual change. The West Ridge of Sgurr nan Gillean, on Skye, used to be adorned by the 'gendarme', a famous pinnacle which featured in the sepia-toned photographs of Victorian climbers. This landmark was prised off the ridge by the spring thaw of 1987 and now lies shattered on the slopes below. On a calm afternoon on the summit of Foinaven, in Sutherland, one can hear the murmurings of shifting scree.

The most dramatic change during the last 11,500 years, however, has been the return of life to a landscape stripped bare by glaciers. The vegetation of the mountains bears the strong imprint of our wild 'oceanic' climate, with mild winters, cool summers and abundant wind and rain. These conditions are uncommon around the world and Scottish mountain vegetation is a distinctive blend with few international parallels.

Trees and woodland

As the temperature rose after the last glaciation, plant life gradually crept northwards into the Scottish mountains, culminating in the development of woodland on lower slopes. This primeval forest reached its peak 6000 years ago without ever forming a continuous blanket, in marked contrast to some romantic images of a 'Great Wood of Caledon'. The tree canopy has retreated greatly since then, at first because of a deteriorating climate and more recently because of felling, grazing and burning. Many Scottish hillslopes are scattered with downy birch and rowan, whose elegant fronds are lit by blazing red berries in autumn. Native pinewoods are relatively common in the colder and drier central and eastern Highlands, and sometimes harbour crested tit or capercaillie in their resin-scented depths.

On many mountains elsewhere in the world, woodland extends to a natural upper limit before fading into low-growing 'alpine' vegetation. Natural treelines now occur on only a handful of Scottish mountains because of the extent of past woodland clearance. At about 600m on Creag Fhiaclach above Glen Feshie, native woodland gives way to a remarkable belt of twisted and contorted 'bonsai pinewood' - a relic of a habitat which was once much more widespread.

14

Scots pine

Rowan

Heaths and bogs

Lower slopes in the north-west are now carpeted by wet heath in which coarse grasses tangle with heather, pink bells of cross-leaved heath and yellow spikes of bog asphodel. This rough vegetation dominates the expansive landscapes of Wester Ross and Sutherland, flowing over and around terraces of Torridonian sandstone. Some wet heath results from woodland clearance, but much could be almost natural, and these wild landscapes may come as close to a primal state as anywhere in Britain. Sheltered slopes and hollows on these mountains can harbour delicate and colourful mixtures of liverworts, which form intricate gold and purple mats beneath the heather canopy.

Poorly-drained hollows in the north-west develop blanket bog with cotton grasses and *Sphagnum* mosses. These living sponges have a remarkable hollow-celled structure which retains water, helping to maintain waterlogged conditions. The resulting microscopic labyrinth contains a complete ecosystem within an ecosystem, with up to 220,000 protozoa per gram of moss. All of these plant communities are characteristically 'oceanic' and Scotland contains 10% of the world's blanket bog.

The lower flanks of the central and eastern Highlands are coloured by the darker hue of vigorous heather and splashed with the lush green of blaeberry. Heaths and bogs hereabouts are also dotted with dwarf shrubs of cold climes such as cow-berry, bearberry and cloudberry - whose solitary berries make excellent gin!

Cross-leaved heath   Bog asphodel

Not surprisingly, the widespread occurrence of heather in the Scottish mountains has resulted in a host of practical uses. These have included roofing, bedding, flooring, ropes, brooms, harrows, baskets, pot scrubbers, beer, wine, tea, dyes and tanning agents. The plant has also been used for medicinal purposes, including the treatment of coughs, colds, insomnia, rheumatism and bladder or kidney complaints.

Flora Celtica - Scotland 2000 database

Plant life on the high tops

Heather is the most talismanic plant of the lower parts of our mountains, but its existence becomes ever more tenuous with increasing altitude. Stunted stems cling to the ground on windswept brows between 600 and 900m, but above this level, exposed slopes and summits are carpeted by *Racomitrium lanuginosum*, or woolly fringe moss. This moss is extremely well adapted to the tops, deriving water and nutrients exclusively from rain and mist. The occasional dry spell does not pose any problem, however, for the plant can also survive total drought for up to a year.

This remarkable moss is also found in other oceanic mountains and tundras, for example in North America, where its soft mats were traditionally used by the Inuit to line funeral biers. Even this plant, however, loses its grip in the extreme environment of the Cairngorm summits. Here, moss heaths are replaced by great expanses of three-leaved rush, anchored in the wind-blown gravel by its tough root system. This distinctive habitat rolls on for mile after mile over the bleak Cairngorm plateau, the rush tussocks quivering in the wind.

The particularly oceanic climate of the far north-west is reflected by exceptionally cool, cloudy summers and frequent strong winds, even by Scottish standards. This combination of influences causes mountain plant communities to develop at unusually low altitudes, and carpets of *Racomitrium* occur on some hills as low as 500m in the Western Isles.

Cowberry

Racomitrium heath on top of Beinn Airigh Charr

Meall à Choire Léith

Snow is integral to the mountain environment and presents plants with both a crisis and an opportunity. A snow blanket provides shelter from the ferocity of winter, with extreme temperatures and lacerating spindrift, but also limits the growing season. Progressively longer snow cover therefore supports distinct communities of plants which are adapted to these conditions. 'Early' snowbeds are marked by grasses and sedges, while more long-lived snows conceal specialised mosses and liverworts, sometimes forming a precarious crust over ground which slumps downhill, laden with meltwater. The warmth of fine August days fails to penetrate the near-permanent snowbeds of Ben Nevis and the Cairngorms, which conceal a dark and silent underworld. Even these snows, however, are an indirect source of life, and their frigid meltwater forms sparkling springs with cushions of mosses and liverworts.

Purple saxifrage

Snowbeds

Our characteristic mountain vegetation is punctuated by a number of habitats or plants of particular rarity. Ben Lawers and neighbouring summits are composed of particularly calcium-rich schist, creating an unusual high altitude niche for alpine plants which are uncommon, or absent, elsewhere in Scotland. On these mountains, lush tangles of colourful tall herbs cascade over crags, while smaller plants form intricate patchworks over unstable gravel scoured by drainage and churned by frost heave. Scattered rocky ledges harbour patches of low-growing downy or woolly willows, their leaves matted with delicate silvery hairs. This is perhaps the rarest habitat in the Scottish mountains, with no more than 0.1km^2 in the whole country. Regeneration of these willows is extremely tenuous, as male and female reproductive structures occur on separate plants which may be up to 50km apart.

Some extreme rarities are confined to just one or two individual mountains within the UK. The conspicuous golden moss *Herbertus borealis* occurs only on Beinn Eighe, while alpine rock-cress is found only on rock ledges high on the Black Cuillin. The tenacious diapensia clings to a single exposed ridge in the western Highlands, pushing up small white flowers in May, and remained entirely undetected until 1951. Other surprises undoubtedly await those who explore the most wild and remote sanctuaries.

"*The haunts of these alpine plants are wild and inspiring. The black corries, where precipices rise sheer for a thousand feet, where broken chimneys and vast heaps of scree encumber the climber and where the snows lie late, it is here that many a rare alpine has its home*".

A.E. Holden 1952

Roseroot growing on a cliff ledge which is inaccessible to sheep or deer

Globeflower

Alpine lady's mantle

Willow scrub

Bearberry

Mountain hare

Red fox

Bellowing stag

Upland mammals

Our upland landscapes are home to a number of larger animals, some of which are icons of Scotland. Perhaps foremost among these are red deer, which are as important for tourism as for the stalking and venison they provide. In the damp half-light of dusk in October, the groans of rutting stags echo round cloud-wreathed corries with primeval energy.

Mountain hares thrive on the heathery grouse moors and hillslopes of the eastern Highlands, sometimes bursting from underfoot as their resting places or forms are disturbed. Foxes also venture onto the higher tops, and their footprints are sometimes the only sign of life on bleak snow-crusted ridges in the depths of winter. On many slopes, however, the most frequently seen creature is actually an amphibian. The humble frog is abundant on most Scottish hills and high, lonely lochans emit a chorus of hoarse croaks on warm spring days.

Upland birds

The birds of the Scottish mountains are particularly evocative. The mournful call of golden plover accentuates the vastness of the tops, while at closer quarters, the croak of ptarmigan can be heard on many rocky summits. The golden eagle is perhaps the perfect epitome of these wild places, soaring and spiralling around such peaks as the jagged Cuillin of Skye. Our mountain birds also include jewels such as dotterel, which nest on the bleak alpine heaths, and sparrow-like snow bunting, which frequent the high, craggy corries. Only a few score of these buntings breed in Scotland, their black and white plumage merging with mosaics of rock and lingering snow. The lower slopes are home to the unmistakeable red grouse, and startled birds erupt from the heather with a rattling machine gun-like alarm call.

Invertebrate life

Birds and mammals are relatively conspicuous, but numerous beetles, spiders, flies, butterflies and moths also frequent the slopes and summits. Lowly invertebrates often form essential links in mountain ecosystems, and the cranefly *Tipula montana*, for example, provides vital food for dotterel. Many of these creatures, such as the red-flecked Mountain Burnett moth, or the dragonflies which patrol dark bog pools, also add extra colour and richness to the mountain scene. Many rarities are confined to a few hills, including the spider *Hilaira nubigena*, whose four Scottish sites include the northern outpost of Ben Hope in Sutherland. These are among the most mysterious aspects of our mountain wildlife and much undoubtedly remains to be discovered.

"With the red deer itself, the golden eagle is the grandest of the wild creatures which fittingly belong to this most extensive and challenging of our mountain regions".

Derek Ratcliffe, 1990, referring to the Highlands

Wildlife often features in the Gaelic names of Scottish hills. Common elements include fraoch (eg. Fraoch Bheinn; heathery mountain), and choinnich (eg. Sgurr Choinnich Mor; big mossy peak). The dark, majestic golden eagle well suits its Gaelic name of iolaire dubh (black eagle), and this name is sometimes applied to crags as, for example, Creag na h-Iolaire.

Dotterel

Red grouse

Emperor moth

Ptarmigan

Mountains and people

People have exerted ever-greater influence on the mountains in recent millennia. The high places were once seen as grim and forbidding, striking terror into early travellers such as Thomas Pennant. In Victorian times, a more romantic view was promoted by artists and writers such as J.M.W. Turner and Sir Walter Scott. This period also saw an awakening of scientific interest, including early botanical exploration and construction of the Ben Nevis observatory. Nowadays, mountains form a common cultural thread extending from 'Monarch of the Glen' to the poetry of Sorley Maclean. For many people, mountains define Scotland itself.

The travel writer Thomas Pennant was struck by An Teallach, which overlooks Dundonnell. In his 'Tour in Scotland' of 1769, he described the mountain as "horrible and awful with summits broken, sharp and serrated and springing into all terrific forms!"

An Teallach, Wester Ross

Extract from Loch Coruisk (JMW Turner, ca 1831)

"To shoot one of these well-proportioned, delicate, beautifully camouflaged and adapted animals is a serious business which gives rise in the rifle to thoughts of his own impermanence and tenuous adherence to life. Set against some of the most beautiful scenery anywhere, in one of the world's oldest and most weathered mountain ranges,...these intimations of mortality can reach a pitch of almost painful acuteness. The hills are eternal, and man is fiery and fit for a brief time".

Michael Wigan 1992

Stalking party

Sheep walks and deer forests

During the last 300 years, human imprints have gradually extended onto the most rugged and remote summits. The lower slopes and straths have long been used for marginal agriculture, although most hill land is of naturally low productivity, and ruined sheilings are a common sight. Many formerly inhabited straths were depopulated during the infamous Clearances of the 18th and 19th centuries, to make way for vast upland sheep-walks. In most parts of the Highlands, this phase was succeeded by the development of sporting estates during the 19th and early 20th centuries, and many imposing shooting lodges date from this period.

Deer stalking is now widespread and is accompanied by grouse shooting on the lower heather moors of the relatively dry central and eastern Highlands, which provide prime grouse habitat. These moors are managed by rotational burning to maintain vigorous heather of varying heights, creating unmistakeable 'patchwork quilt' markings. These activities provide livelihoods for farmers, stalkers, gamekeepers and other land managers, and support jobs further downstream in, for example, the venison industry.

Sheep farming

Muirburn patchwork

Hillwalker above Loch Coruisk, Skye

Hillwalking and mountaineering

The growth of these activities has been paralleled by an expansion of other types of recreation, notably mountaineering. The Cairngorm and Scottish Mountaineering Clubs were founded in 1887 and 1889 respectively, and Sir Hugh Munro's famous Tables were first published shortly afterwards in 1891. This mighty feat of surveying gave birth to a national cult activity and over 2700 pilgrims have since completed all of the 3000ft 'Munro' summits. Some estimates suggest that hillwalkers may number 10% of the Scottish population.

Climbing has also grown in popularity and sophistication, starting from early ventures equipped with perilously thin ropes which, it was said, 'served only to maintain the illusion that man is a gregarious animal'. The spectacular crags of Skye, Glencoe, Ben Nevis and the Cairngorms have attracted all of the leading lights in British mountaineering and now provide a wealth of established climbs. The high ridges and plateaux, particularly in the central and eastern Highlands, are also popular for ski-touring when snow permits.

Scotland's upland landscapes are a mainstay of our tourism industry. Mountain recreation is probably the largest source of income and employment in Scotland's hill regions, and many visitors also savour dramatic mountain scenery from low level walks and viewpoints.

Rock climbing on Ben Nevis

30

Bidean nam Bian from Buachaille Etive Beag

"On a bad day, if it was cold, late or otherwise ill-starred, the feeling might well begin to niggle: 'This is no place to be'. But the buttress is so handsome, the vistas of the Torridon mountains so tremendously sculpted, and I am so ready to lose my bothered self in physical grapple with the wilderness that nothing can baffle our momentum".

David Craig on Mainreachan Buttress, Fuar Tholl 1987

Beinn Alligin

Red deer in woodland

Human impacts

Although mountains provide great benefits to the people of Scotland, human activity can also have detrimental effects on this environment. Excessive numbers of grazing sheep restrict the development of native woodland and suppress the growth of heather, which is gradually replaced by coarse grassland. In the absence of predators such as wolves, deer populations can also become very large, and more rigorous culling is needed in many areas to achieve a balance with woodland and moorland habitats. Burning is often used in the management of sheep walks and grouse moors, and poorly controlled fires can exacerbate these detrimental effects.

Vehicle tracks, telecommunication masts and hydro-electricity schemes have introduced development, not always appropriately, within our mountain landscapes. Lower hill slopes often carry extensive conifer plantations, which are particularly extensive in the Southern Uplands, but new approaches to forestry are beginning to address these problems and nurture native woodland. A few mountains have even suffered because of their own popularity and are scarred by path erosion.

Some of the most pervasive effects on Scotland's mountains arise from activities elsewhere and are very hard to tackle. Global warming could reduce the extent of alpine habitats, but renewable energy developments, if sited in our wilder mountain areas, could also erode their quality. Air pollution has contributed to a decline of *Racomitrium* heaths in some parts of southern Scotland, although such pollution may now be decreasing.

Action to tackle all of these problems will be a measure of our commitment to protect this mountain heritage.

A well worn track

Walker above Loch Linnhe, Lochaber

Looking ahead

The stewardship of Scotland's mountains presents a formidable challenge, but there is also cause for optimism. Our understanding of the mountain environment, and its value to society, is greater now than ever before. Wild mountain landscapes are increasingly recognised as economic assets, as well as places for nature and spiritual refreshment. The UN International Year of Mountains, in 2002, symbolises the importance which is now accorded to these areas.

Scotland's new National Parks in Loch Lomond & the Trossachs and the Cairngorms should be well placed to develop new approaches to conservation and land management, and to demonstrate how the enhancement of mountain areas can benefit local communities and the nation as a whole. The planning system has an important role in preventing inappropriate development across all of the Scottish uplands. But responsibility for the mountains is shared to varying degrees by all who have an interest in these magnificent areas, including land managers, public bodies, Non-Government Organisations and those who use the hills for recreation. The challenge ahead will be for these bodies and individuals to work together, with a shared commitment to safeguard and enhance our mountain resource.

"By taking care of the world's mountains, we help to ensure the long-term security and survival of all that is connected to them, including ourselves.".

FAO/UN IYM website, 2002

Dawn over Slioch and Loch Maree, Wester Ross

35

Beinn Eighe, Wester Ross

References

Craig, D. (1987). *Native Stones*. Flamingo.

Geikie, A. (1901). *The Scenery of Scotland*. Macmillan.

Holden, A.E. (1952). *Plant life in the Scottish Highlands*. Oliver and Boyd.

Kilgour, W.T. (1905). *Twenty Years on Ben Nevis*. Ernest Press.

Ratcliffe, D. (1990). *Bird life of Mountain and Upland*. Cambridge University Press.

Pennant, T. (1769). *Tour in Scotland*. Birlinn Publishers.

United Nations (1992). *Agenda 21; UN Conference on Environment and Development, Rio*.

Whittow, J. (1992). *Geology and Scenery in Britain*. Chapman and Hall.

Wigan, M. (1992) in: *The Highland Game: Life on Scottish Sporting Estates*. Glyn Satterley. Swan Hill Press.

Addresses

Please contact SNH at the address below, or your local Area office, for further information about the natural heritage, or sustainable management, of Scotland's mountains. Practical demonstrations of upland management for landscape and biodiversity benefits are provided by a number of National Nature Reserves (NNR) owned by SNH.

Scottish Natural Heritage
2 Anderson Place
EDINBURGH
EH6 5NP
Tel: 0131 447 4784
www.snh.org.uk

Some other organisations which are closely involved in the positive management of mountain areas:

The National Trust for Scotland
Wemyss House
28 Charlotte Square
EDINBURGH
EH2 4ET
Tel: 0131 243 9300
E-mail: information@nts.org

The John Muir Trust
41 Commercial Street
EDINBURGH
EH6 6JD
Tel: 0131 554 0114
E-mail: admin@jmt.org

RSPB (Scotland)
Dunedin House
25 Ravelston Terrace
EDINBURGH
EH4 3TP
Tel: 0131 311 6500
E-mail: rspb.scotland@rspb.org.uk

The Scottish Wildlife Trust
Cramond House
Kirk Cramond
Cramond Glebe Road
EDINBURGH
EH4 6NS
Tel: 0131 312 7765
E-mail: enquiries@swt.org.uk

The Mountaineering Council of Scotland
The Old Granary
West Mill Street
PERTH
PH1 5QP
Tel: 01738 638227
E-mail: info@mountaineering.scotland.org.uk

Also in Scotland's Living Landscapes series

If you have enjoyed Mountains why not find out more about Scotland's distinctive habitats in our Scotland's Living Landscapes series. Each 'landscape' is a dynamic environment supporting a wealth of plants and animals, whose lives are woven inextricably together. The colourfully illustrated booklets explore these complex relationships simply and concisely, and explain why they are important and what needs to be done to protect them for the future.

Sea Lochs

Featuring dramatic underwater photography, this booklet tells why Scotland's sea lochs are so special to people living around their shores and to the magnificent wildlife that depends on their sheltered waters.
Sue Scott
ISBN 1 85397 246 0 pbk 24pp £3.00

Firths

Firths lie at the heart of Scottish life: they support our economy, house most of our population, and provide a precious home for wildlife. Discover the magic of our unsung firths and the efforts being made to secure their future.
Steve Atkins
ISBN 1 85397 271 1 pbk 36pp £3.50

Machair

Machair is a rare coastal habitat widely recognised for its swathes of colourful wildflowers and abundant bird life. Find out how machair resulted from natural forces combined with centuries of careful land management.
John Love
ISBN 1 85397 001 8 pbk 28pp £3.00

Coasts

Scotland has nearly 12,000km of coastline, much of it remote, unspoilt and strikingly beautiful. Learn all about this changing environment, the unique habitats, landforms and wildlife and the many pressures they face.
George Lees & Kathy Duncan
ISBN 1 85397 003 4 pbk 28pp £3.00

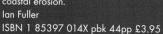

Boglands

Bogland is one of Britain's most undervalued habitats. This booklet challenges the conventional view of boglands and rewards its reader with vivid images of the colourful and intriguing wildlife of bogs.
Richard Lindsay
ISBN 1 85397 120 2 pbk 20pp £3.95

Soils

As all gardeners know, what grows on the surface depends on what's beneath their feet. Indeed soils are home to a all sorts of animals as well as plants. This booklet relates the story of our soils to the landscapes we see everyday.
Andrew Taylor & Stephen Nortcliff
ISBN 1 85397 223 1 pbk 24pp £2.50

Kelp Forests

An essential introduction to this hidden kingdom. Discover the variety of plants and animals which live in the 'forests', find out why kelp forests are so important in Scottish waters and how healthy kelp forests help to prevent coastal erosion.
Ian Fuller
ISBN 1 85397 014X pbk 44pp £3.95

Grasslands

Grasslands form an important part of our natural heritage and this booklet looks at how they provide a vital habitat for birds, butterflies, animals and plants.
Stephen Ward & Jane MacKintosh
ISBN 1 85397 070 0 pbk 48pp £3.95